M000033018

TWO HEARTS

The Greeks

Tana Reiff

A Pacemaker® **HOPES** *and* **DREAMS 2** Book

FEARON/JANUS/QUERCUS
Belmont, California

Simon & Schuster Supplementary Education Group

HOPES *and* DREAMS 2

Cover photo: The Granger Collection, New York
Cover Design: Rucker Huggins
Illustration: Duane Bibby

ISBN 0–8224–3805–4
Library of Congress Catalog Card Number: 92–71064

Printed in the United States of America
1. 9 8 7 6 5 4 3
MA

CONTENTS

1 Sister Needs a Husband

A mountain village in Greece, 1911

"We are as poor as dirt,"
said George Stavros's mother.
"Until you are old enough
to make money,
our only hope
is for your sister
to get a good husband.
But how do we find
a good husband for her?
We have no dowry—
no gift of money
for a man.
Your father is dead.
And Greece is in a sorry state.
Many men are out of work
and cannot find jobs.
So what can we do?"

George's sister Adonia
was dark and pretty.

But being pretty
was not as important
as having money.
And the more money
a family had,
the better the husband
a young woman might get.

"Poor Adonia,"
said Mama.
"Look at her."

George's sister
sat by the one window
of the little house.
"Maybe I could find
a good man
even if we have no money,"
said Adonia.

"You dream,"
said Mama.
"I have high hopes
for my children.

You will not marry
just any low person
who comes along."

Mama rocked in her chair.
Like any Greek woman
who had lost her husband,
she wore only black.
She would wear only black
until the day she died.
She was only 40 years old.
She had four more children
besides George and Adonia.
She had no hope
of ever having
another husband of her own.
Her only hope
was for her children.

George began to sing.
"I want to go
to far-away lands.
To far-away lands
I must go."

"What is this song?"
Mama asked.

"It's about America,"
said George.
"All the boys
sing this song.
In fact, Mama,
a man spoke
with some of us boys
about going to America.
He has jobs lined up for us.
I could go and make money
to find a husband
for Adonia."

Mama looked at George.
"You mean to tell me
Greek boys can go
to such a far-away land,
and they can work there?"
said Mama.
She stopped speaking,
as if she were thinking
about something.
Then she said,

"I will tell you
what I think.
George, you should go
to America.
Send us money
for your sister.
We will be all right here
until you come home."

But when the day came
for George to leave,
Mama was not so ready
to see him go.
There were tears
in her eyes.
He and the other boys
kissed their mothers good-bye.
They walked in a line
down the mountain.
Each boy carried
a heavy pack
on his back.
George turned around
for one more look
at the village.
The little houses

seemed like tiny white boxes
against the green mountain.
He could see the open fields
high up the mountain
where he used to watch
his little herd of goats.
George would never forget
those happy days.
He did not want to leave.
This was home—
the mountain, the village,
and Greece itself.
George wondered
if he would ever again
see anything so beautiful.
Yet he couldn't wait
to make a good dowry
for dear Adonia.

At the bottom
of the mountain,
George picked up
a little, round gray stone.
He kept it
in his pocket
the whole trip.

Thinking It Over

1. What do you think
   of the idea
   of giving money
   to get a good husband?

2. Would you go
   to a "far-away land"
   just so your sister
   could find a husband?

3. Is George smart
   to trust the man
   who said he has jobs
   lined up for the boys?
   Why or why not?

2 The Shoe-Shine Boy

When George and his friends
set foot in New York,
some men met them
at Ellis Island.
"Come with me,"
said one man to George.
"I am your *padrone*.
I will take you
to your job."
He took George
to a busy street
in the busy city.
They turned down
a little side street.
There was trash
on the ground.
They went inside
one of the buildings.
George followed the *padrone*
up the stairs

to the fifth floor.
They walked to a room
at the end of a dark hall.

"You will sleep here
each night,"
said the *padrone*.
"That bed in the corner is yours.
You will share this room
with six other Greek boys."

George didn't like the room.
Nor did he like the building.
It smelled bad in the hall,
and it smelled bad in the room.
But he said nothing
to the *padrone*.
Soon they were walking
on the busy street again.
When they came
to a bootblack shop,
they stepped inside.

"You will shine shoes here,"
the man told George.

"Meet your boss, Mr. Kostas.
This is his shop.
You will work here,
and Mr. Kostas will see
that you get enough
food to eat.
Now I must be off.
I'll stop back soon
and check on you."
The man tipped his hat
and left the little shop.

"See here how
to do a perfect spit shine!"
Mr. Kostas told George.
The boy watched as Mr. Kostas
ran the shoe-shine rag
over the first shoe.
Mr. Kostas made the rag
fly back and forth.
George wondered
how he could ever work
as fast as Mr. Kostas.

But every day,
George worked faster.

Men in business suits
came in off the street.
From 6:00 A.M. to 9:00 P.M.,
George shined
their shoes and boots
until he could see
his own face in the toes.
His arms, neck, and back
were very stiff
by the end of each long day.

But none of this
was good enough for Mr. Kostas.
"Why do they send me
lazy bums like you?"
the boss would say.
"You and I—
we're stuck with each other.
And don't try
to get away from me, either!
I'll tell your *padrone,*
and heaven only knows
what he'll do to you.
So get on the stick!
Work better!
Work faster!"

George didn't know
how to please Mr. Kostas.
The one good part
was that he made friends
with one of the older boys
in the shop.
"When do we get paid?"
George asked Gus
after a few months
on the job.

"I get paid next month,"
said the boy, Gus.
"I make 20 dollars a year."

"Will I get 20 dollars, too?"
George asked.

"Not you,"
said Gus.
"You won't get a cent
until you finish
your first year here."

"No pay for a year?"
George asked.

"That's the plan,"
said Gus.

"I came here
to make money fast,"
said George.
"Now I'm stuck
in this bootblack shop,
working for nothing!"
He was almost crying.

"You're not stuck,"
said Gus.
"If you don't like it here,
you can walk out
anytime you wish.
Mr. Kostas can't do anything
to get you in trouble."

"Why don't you leave?"
George asked Gus.

"Well, I would have to find
a place to live,"
said Gus.
"The *padrones*

are not kind people.
But they do keep
a roof over our heads.
Besides, if I worked
in a mill up north instead,
I would make
only 10 or 15 dollars a year.
You put in some time here,
and it pays off."

George didn't feel right
about any of this news.
He couldn't see himself
working a whole year
for nothing.
He didn't know what to do.
Then an old friend
from his village
let him know
there were restaurant jobs uptown.

One morning
George didn't come to work.
He headed uptown
and he never returned
to the bootblack shop.

Thinking It Over

1. What would you have done
   if you were "in George's shoes"?

2. For what reasons
   do people fall for deals
   that are not fair to them?

3. If you were George,
   would you have told Mr. Kostas
   that you were leaving?
   Why or why not?

3 Hard Work for Nothing

George was lucky.
He slept
on the streets of New York
only three nights
before he found work
and a place to live.

The sign
on the restaurant window
read, "HELP WANTED."
George knew enough English
to read this.

He walked inside
and found the owner.
"Nice restaurant,"
he said in English.
"Work here?"

"No speak-y English, huh?"
laughed the owner, Mr. Carter.

"No matter.
You don't need to speak
to clear tables!
But I can't take you on
looking like that."

George saw himself
in the window.
He looked a mess.
One empty pocket
hung out of his pants.

"I'll tell you what,"
said Mr. Carter.
"I have rooms upstairs.
Running water, too.
I will pay you
a little less each week
and you can live up there."

George's face lit up.
He understood
what Mr. Carter was saying.

"Now go upstairs
and clean yourself up,"

said Mr. Carter.
He threw a white shirt and pants
into George's arms.
"Put those on
and come back downstairs.
I need you right away."

So once again
George was working
long hours for low pay.
But he didn't mind.
Every day,
he thanked Mr. Carter
for giving him a job.
And every week,
he sent home
a few more cents
to put toward Adonia's dowry.
"This is great,"
he said to himself often.
"Come to America
and get work,
just like that!"

The months went by.
Then one day,

George got a letter
from his mother.
"Dowry or no dowry,
you must come home,"
she wrote.
"There's a war on here.
Greece needs its young men
to fight the Turks."*

George spent
all the money he had
to pay for the ship home.
He had to help Greece.
He wanted to help Greece.
But he was sick in his heart.
He was going back
without a dowry for Adonia
and not a penny in his pocket.
He felt as if
his year in America had been
a complete waste of time.

---

*In the two Balkan Wars of 1912 and
 1913, Greece and its allies, Bulgaria,
 Serbia, and Montenegro, defeated Turkey.
 Then Bulgaria turned on its allies, but
 it was defeated.

Thinking It Over

1. Do you think
   that George's time in America
   was "a complete waste of time"?

2. If you were living
   in a country other than your own,
   would you go back
   to your own country
   to fight in a war?

3. Suppose you were Mr. Carter.
   Why would you give
   George a job?

4 Second Time Around

And so, in 1912,
George Stavros
was back in Greece.
A little older now,
he joined the army.
By the next year,
the fighting was over.

Once again,
men came to the village
to find strong young men
to work in America.
George needed work.
Adonia still needed a husband.
Mama said
that George should go.

This time,
George went to Chicago
to work in a factory.
His job was to put pieces

into machines.
He stood all day,
as each machine
came down the line.
He had to be quick
and watch out
for his fingers.
He hated
every minute of it.
He hated working
by the hour.
He hated being cooped up
in a hot factory.

George lived
in a large house
with other young men.
The house
was in Chicago's Greektown.
George was happy
to have work
and friends from his village.
But this life
was really not much
to be happy about.

So it was a big lift
when a new Greek church
was built in Greektown.

   Now there was
a place to go.
George and his friends
could pray and sing,
just like in Greece.
There were dinners
of lamb and salad
and Greek pastries.
There were many new friends,
and even young women
to get to know.

   George always knew
he would marry
a Greek woman.
He did not know
he would meet that woman
in America.
Her name was Daphne.
He met her
at a church dinner.

It must have been
love at first sight.
For the next few days,
George could think of
nothing but Daphne.

He saw her again
the next Sunday
at the church.
Daphne seemed to have
just as much interest in George
as he had in her.
As the weeks went by,
they became close friends.

One day,
Daphne and George
were walking in the park.
"Wouldn't it be nice
if we were married?"
said Daphne.

George stopped walking.
He felt torn by these words.
Nothing would be better
than to marry Daphne.

But he knew
this was not possible.

"I tell you right now,
we cannot get married
until I make my sister's dowry,"
George told Daphne.
"And I have
a long way to go.
Then, I will return to Greece.
That is the plan."

"I understand,"
said Daphne.
"After all, I have no dowry
to give to you.
We don't have dowries
in America."

But as months went by,
George began to believe
that he could not stand
to stay in the factory.
"It looks as if
I must return home early,"
he told Daphne.

"Can't you find
another line of work here?"
she asked.

"Well, I've been thinking,"
George began.
"It might be fun
to buy a pushcart
and sell ice cream on the street.
I'd be outside all day
in the fresh air
meeting new people.
I need money
to get started, however."

"Selling ice cream!
That's a fine idea!"
said Daphne.
"Would you give me
free ice cream?"

"I'll give you ice cream
for what it costs me!"
laughed George.
"If I give it all away,
I'll never make any money!"

Thinking It Over

1. If you were selling something,
   would you give it away
   to your friends?
   Why or why not?

2. How do you go about
   getting something
   for which you don't have
   enough money?

3. Would you rather
   work in a factory
   or sell things?

5 Selling Ice Cream

George saved his money.
At last, he had enough
to buy an old pushcart.
One day Daphne was walking
down the street.
There, in the window
of a new Greek restaurant,
she spotted a sign that said,
"PUSHCART FOR SALE."
Its owner must have started
with a pushcart
and then opened a restaurant.

"Maybe you could do
the same thing!"
she said to George.
"Start with a pushcart
and then open a restaurant!"

"One thing at a time,"
George said.

He bought the pushcart.
He changed it
so that it could hold ice cream
for hours at a time.
He left his factory job.
Then he hit the streets
with his new business.

"Ice cream! Ice cream!
Five cents a dish!"
he called,
from his favorite corner.
Everyone loved ice cream.
That's why George Stavros
made good money selling it.

Still, there were bad days.
One morning he pushed his cart
to the corner.
Much to his surprise,
another man and pushcart
were already there.

"Hey, what are you
doing on my corner?"
George called to the man.

"Selling hot dogs,"
the man answered back.

"This is my corner!"
said George.
"You find your own spot!"

"I'm doing pretty well
right where I am,"
said the man.

George put up a fist.
"You better move!"
he shouted.
That was enough
to scare the man away.
The man took his cart
and found another place
to sell his hot dogs.

Every few weeks,
George had a run-in
with someone else
trying to work his space.
He was beginning to believe
he owned that corner.

Thinking It Over

1. If you wanted
   to start a business,
   what would it be?

2. What would you
   have to do
   to get your business going?

3. Do you feel
   that you own
   the street you live on?
   What makes you feel that way?

6 Time to Marry

Two years later,
George still sold ice cream
on the street.
Now he also sold it in cones
and with fancy toppings.

Daphne still waited
to marry George.
Back in Greece,
Adonia still waited
for a husband.
George had sent home
enough money for a fine dowry.
But Adonia had no husband
because almost all the young men
from the village
had gone to America.

"Now what do I do?"
George said to Daphne.
"My sister has a dowry.

I have done my job for her.
But how can I
return to Greece
when I am making money
here in America?"

"What do you want to do?"
Daphne asked him.

"I want to find
a little store in Greektown,"
said George.
"I want to start
an ice cream shop!
I can't do that
back in Greece."

"Then do it here,"
said Daphne.
"I will help you."

"I also want to marry you,"
said George.
"I make enough money now
for both of us to live on.
What do you say?"

Daphne threw her arms
around George.
"I would love to marry you!
I'll tell my parents!
We'll have a big Greek wedding!"

"Good! Good!"
George said.
"First we will marry.
Then we will start
our ice cream shop."

"Wait a minute,"
said Daphne.
"I will marry you
only if the ice cream shop
stays closed on Sundays."

"I sell a lot of ice cream
on Sundays now,"
said George.

"No Sundays,"
said Daphne.
"Church and family
are more important than money."

"Very well,"
said George.
"No Sundays."

George and Daphne
got married
in the new Greek church.
They did not send out cards
asking people to the wedding.
Everyone in Greektown
knew they were welcome.

"There must be
400 people here!"
George whispered to Daphne
as they danced
at their wedding.

"Five hundred if there's one!"
laughed Daphne.
"And most of them
brought along some Greek food
that they made themselves!"

"It is all wonderful,"
said George.

"Now what kinds of ice cream
should we sell in our shop?"

"Can't you ever
get your mind off business?"
Daphne asked.
She wasn't really angry.
She was as ready as George
to open a shop.

Not long after
they got married,
they did open that shop.
It was a tiny space
that opened onto the street.
There was room for one freezer
full of ice cream.
There was room
for two or three people
to stand by the counter
and order a favorite kind.
There were no tables.
Just ice cream,
hungry people,
George, Daphne,
and a money box.

But the only thing
that felt crowded
was the money box.
It filled up so fast
that George had to go
to the bank
four times a day.

The first few weeks,
two signs hung in the window.
One said, "ICE CREAM."
The other said,
"PUSHCART FOR SALE."
Then one day
a young man from Greece
bought the old pushcart.

George took down
the pushcart sign.
That was the day he knew
he had two hearts.
One of them
was still back in Greece.
The other,
George now knew,
would stay in America.

Thinking It Over

1. George felt as if
   he had two hearts.
   How many hearts
   do you have?
   Where are they?

2. If you were George,
   where would you
   choose to live?
   Why?

3. These days,
   how would you
   go about selling something
   you wanted to get rid of?

7 A Growing Business

Over the next few years,
George and Daphne
had three children.
They named the two girls
Phoebe and Myra.
They named the boy Andreas,
but they called him Andy.

As soon as the children
began to walk,
they were helping out
in the ice cream shop.
They could say,
"vanilla" and "chocolate"
before they could say
their last name.

Everyone who came in said,
"What sweet children!"
But people
were used to seeing children

working in a family business.
There were children
in all the businesses in Greektown.
"We start the work habit
early around here,"
Daphne would laugh.

Andy took the most interest.
By the time
he was six years old,
he was scooping ice cream.
By the time he was 14 years old,
he was working as much
as his parents.
By the time he was 16,
he asked to be paid.
By the time he was 18,
he had his own ideas
for running the business.
Sometimes he forgot
that his father was the boss,
in both the family
and the business.

"Bamba, don't you think
it's time for this business

to grow?"
Andy asked George one day.

"What do you mean?"
George asked his son.
"We make a good living.
You children never go hungry.
What do you mean—grow?"

"Well, some people
who come in here
ask me why
we don't have tables,"
said Andy.
"I say to them,
'Where would we put tables?'
Anyone can see there's no room
to turn around in here."

"What's wrong with that?"
asked George.

"Well, I was thinking,"
Andy said.
"Why don't we find a bigger shop
where we can fit tables?"

"That sounds to me
like a restaurant,"
said George.

"That's the idea!"
said Andy.
"Let's turn our business
into a restaurant!"

"Let me think about it,"
said George.

Andy was surprised
when a few days later
his father said,
"I've been thinking.
Let's open a restaurant."
George made it sound
like his own idea.

"Great idea, Bamba!"
said Andy.
"A place down the street
is for rent right now.
Let's take a look."

Thinking It Over

1. Think of one kind
   of small business.
   In what ways
   could that business grow?

2. Have you ever known anyone
   who turns everything around
   to make it sound
   like his or her own idea?
   Have you ever done that?

3. How much of a part
   do you think
   children should play
   in a family business?

8 Running a Restaurant

George knew
about the restaurant business
from his days in New York.
He planned his restaurant
in every way.
He was the one who decided
where each table should go.
He was the one who decided
what color the tablecloths should be.
He was the one who decided
what foods should be
on the menu.
He was the one who decided
just how much cheese
to put in the spinach pie.
Everything here
was done George's way.
The whole family
worked in the new restaurant.
But George didn't let them
decide much of anything.

So when Andy married Cleo,
George was not ready
for one more person
in the family business.
He surely wasn't ready
for Cleo.

Cleo was
a beautiful Greek woman.
She was also a person
not afraid to speak her mind.
"So this is your restaurant,"
she said to Andy
the first day she walked in.
"Why in the world
do you have green tablecloths?"

"Bamba says
the green makes him think
of the mountains in Greece,"
Andy explained.

"The tablecloths should be red,"
said Cleo.
"No question about it.
Red makes people hungry."

That's the way things went
when Cleo was around.
No matter how well
things were going,
Cleo always had a better idea.

"You should let your wife know
who's boss around here,"
George whispered to Andy one day.
"In Greece
no woman would get away
with the things Cleo says."

"This isn't Greece,"
said Andy.

"I know that,"
said George.
"But we are Greek.
Greek men are in charge.
I'm in charge
of this restaurant.
You're in charge
of your wife.
Understand, son?"

"There's no stopping Cleo,"
said Andy.
"She's full of life."

"Well, if you ask me,
she should keep her ideas
to herself,"
said George.

"That's enough, Bamba,"
said Andy.
"I'll have a talk
with Cleo.
She's a member
of the family now.
I want the two of you
to get along."

That night
he had a talk with Cleo.
"You have to understand
the way Bamba was brought up,"
said Andy.
"Men come first
in his way of thinking."

"This from a man
who came to America
to give his sister a dowry?"
Cleo laughed.
"Listen, Andy.
I was raised
by Greek parents, too.
They taught me a lot
about the restaurant business.
I do know
what I'm talking about."

"I know you do,"
said Andy.
"But can't you give your ideas
without making Bamba so angry?"

"I'll work on it,"
said Cleo.
"I love your father.
He just doesn't know it yet."

Thinking It Over

1. Do you agree with George
   that Andy should be
   "in charge of" his wife?
   Why or why not?

2. Do you think
   that Cleo has a right
   to give her ideas
   about the restaurant?

3. Did you ever
   know more about a job
   than the person
   you worked under?
   How did you handle this?

9 A Trip to Greece

Things between George and Cleo
got a little better
in the years that followed.
They still had some fights
over how to run things, however.
So when George said
that he and Daphne
were going on a trip,
Cleo was rather glad.
She was sure
a little space
between her and George
would be good for everyone.

"Your mama and I
are going to Greece!"
George told the family.
"I can't stay away
for another day!
I must see my home again
before I die."

Cleo looked at Andy
and rolled her eyes.
"All these years here
and he still doesn't
call Chicago home?"
she whispered.

Andy shook his head.
"Chicago's home to me,"
he said.
"But remember,
Bamba came here with the idea
of going back someday.
He's done very well here,
but he still loves Greece."

"We will leave
on Friday morning,"
said George.
"Phoebe and Myra
will drive us to the airport.
Cleo, you keep an eye
on the house
while we are away.
Andy, you run the restaurant.
And all of you

be sure to go to church
every Sunday!
The big Greek dinner is coming up.
I want you all to help out."

Cleo rolled her eyes again.
"Why am I the one
to watch the house?
You have two sisters,"
she whispered to Andy.

"He's probably afraid
you'll change something
at the restaurant,"
said Andy.
"Don't worry.
I need your help
to run the restaurant."

So George and Daphne
took a trip to Greece.
When George saw
the old village again,
everything seemed the same—
at first.
The little houses

still looked like tiny white boxes
against the green mountain.
Mama was gone now,
but Adonia lived
in the same old place.
Everything was still beautiful.
Yet something felt very different.
George just couldn't
put his finger on what.

Both times he left here,
he was still a boy, really.
Now he was a man
with children and grandchildren
and a life of his own
in America.
That was different
from the way things once were.

George and Daphne
had more money
than they ever dreamed of.
They were not rich,
but they were well off.
They owned a business,
three houses,

and two cars.
That was different
from the way things once were.

Still, George
could not put his finger
on what felt different.

George, Daphne, and Adonia
visited places in Greece
that none of them
had ever seen before.
They went to the islands
and rode in a little boat
with a white sail.
They went to Athens
and saw the great old buildings
they had only seen pictures of.
But Athens was dirty and crowded.
"Chicago is much nicer
than this!"
George said.

When they returned
to the village,
George wasn't talking.

"What's the matter?"
asked Daphne.
"This isn't like you."

"We have visited
all these beautiful places,"
said George.
"But that's just it.
It's been a visit.
I am ready to return to Chicago
and get back
to my business and my family."

Daphne smiled at her husband.
"I feel the same way,"
she said.
"Greece has been in wars
and hard times.
Still, in many ways,
it has not changed
over the years.
But we have.
You are a man
of two hearts, George Stavros.
One of those hearts
has found a home in America."

Thinking It Over

1. Why was it important
   for George to visit Greece?

2. Have you ever visited
   a place you hadn't seen
   for many years?
   What did it feel like
   to see that place again?

3. What do you think
   might happen at the restaurant
   while George and Daphne
   are in Greece?

10 Red Tablecloths

George and Daphne
were away for two months.
When they got back to Chicago,
the first thing George did
was to go over to the restaurant.
He was very surprised
at what he found there.

When he first walked in,
he was sure
he was in the wrong restaurant.
The tablecloths were red.
Then he heard Andy's voice.
"Bamba, you're home!"

"What's going on here?"
George asked his son.

Just then Cleo
stepped out of the kitchen.
"I waited ten years

to change those tablecloths,"
she said.
"I hope you like them."

    "To tell the truth,
I do like them,"
said George.
"They make the place
nice and bright.
Did you change the menus, too?"

    Andy handed George
a new, red menu.
George opened it up.
"What's this—
fried chicken,
hamburgers,
PIZZA?!
This is a Greek restaurant,
not American or Italian.
What have you done
to my restaurant?"

    "People these days
want more than Greek food,"
he said,

as he pulled out a paper
to show his father.
"Look at these numbers, Bamba!
We did more business
in the last two months
than any two months ever!"

   "I'm always glad
to see big numbers
on the books,"
said George.
"But I feel as if
you two have stabbed me
in the heart!
You took over my restaurant
while I was away.
I will never go away again!"

   "Be happy
we take such an interest
in the business,"
said Cleo.
But George was not happy.

   The next morning,
George did not show up

at the restaurant.
"Bamba must be very angry,"
said Andy.

Then, at noon,
George walked in.
"Big news, everyone!"
he called out.
"I just signed a lease.
I am going to open
a new Greek restaurant
on the other side of town."

"Are you crazy?"
Andy asked his father.

"You bet I'm crazy!"
said George.
"You two
can run this restaurant.
Daphne and I
will run the new one."

"What about Phoebe and Myra?"
Andy asked.

"Phoebe would rather
go to school
all her life,"
said George.
"Myra and her husband
are doing pretty well
running their movie house.
The rest of us
are the restaurant people.
Now, what did you do
with those old green menus
and green tablecloths?
I could use them
at the new place."

Thinking It Over

1. What would you have done
   if you were George—
   try to get Andy and Cleo
   to change things back
   or start a new restaurant?
   Why?

2. Have you ever done something
   that you felt was good
   but another person
   felt was bad?

3. What would be
   more important to you—
   doing business your own way
   or making more money?

11 A Chain of Restaurants

George's new restaurant
did well from the start.
Most of the people
who ate there
were not Greek.
For these people
on the other side of town,
Greek dishes
were new and different.
But after a few years,
George found himself
adding American dishes
to his menu.

Having his own restaurant again
helped George get along better
with Andy and Cleo.
One day Andy said,
"Bamba, I'm ready
to open another restaurant.
Why don't we do it together?"

"Greek or American?"
George wanted to know.

"Let's have both,"
said Andy.
"We can serve
mostly American food,
with a few good Greek dishes
that everyone likes.
What do you say?"

"Why not?"
said George.
"We can handle
three restaurants."

So father and son
went to the bank together.
They got a loan
to open another restaurant.
"What will you call
the new place?"
asked the banker.

"I've been thinking
about names,"

said George.
"All three restaurants
are ending up
to be pretty much alike.
I think that all three
should have the same name.
What do you think, Andy?"

Andy had been half surprised
that his father
hadn't turned around
the idea for a third restaurant
to sound like his own idea.
He couldn't believe
that his father
was now *asking*
for his idea on something.

"Well, if we use
the same name
for all three restaurants,
we might as well
have the same menu
for all three,"
said Andy.
"We might as well

make them all
look the same, too.
Having them all the same
would make them easy to run."

"I have just the name,"
said George.
"All three restaurants
can be called *George's.*"

"That's the name
of the first one,"
laughed Andy.

"All right, then,"
said George.
"You get my point.
It's a good name."

Andy shook his father's hand.
"We'll have a whole chain
of George's restaurants!"
said Andy.
"We have come a long way
from ice cream,
haven't we, Bamba?"

Thinking It Over

1. What does it mean
   to "come a long way"
   from something?
   What have you
   "come a long way" from?

2. What changes can you make
   to help get along better
   with someone?

3. What "chains"
   of stores or restaurants
   do you know of?

12 Soft Hearts

With the third restaurant,
George was never so busy.
He was having a ball.
And it was nice
to do all this
with Andy, and even Cleo.

Everything would have been perfect
if Daphne hadn't gotten sick.
The doctors said
it was cancer.
They did all they could for her,
but in just six months,
she was dead.

George's heart was broken.
He didn't know
what to do with himself.
So he spent all his time
running the restaurants.

He hopped
from one to another.
He kept everything running
like a well-oiled machine.
But George Stavros
was not a young man now.
Keeping three restaurants going
was starting to wear on him.

One morning
he was having trouble
getting out of bed.
At last he set one foot
on the floor.
He felt as if
he would fall over.
So he called his doctor.

"I'm sending over
an ambulance,"
said the doctor.
"I'll meet you at the hospital."

George was rushed
to the hospital.

"You had a mild heart attack,"
the doctor told him.
"You must take it easy
for a few months."

"Me, take life easy?"
laughed George.
"You must be kidding!"

"I'm not kidding,"
said the doctor.
"You were lucky this time.
But if you don't
rest and slow down,
one more heart attack
could kill you."

Andy and Cleo
came to visit him
that night.
"What will I do?"
George asked them.
"Who will take care of me?
Phoebe took that teaching job
in North Carolina.
Myra and her family

are all tied up
with their movie houses.
I don't want
to go into a nursing home.
That's not the Greek way."

Neither Andy nor Cleo
made a sound.
Then Cleo began to speak.
"I'll take care of you,"
she said.
George had never heard her
speak in such a soft voice.
It was full of love
as he had never heard
from his daughter-in-law.

"You?" George asked.

"I mean it, Bamba,"
said Cleo.
"We can work things out
with the restaurants.
They can almost
run themselves."
She took George's hand.

"Come and live
with Andy and me."

And so Cleo
took care of George
for the next few months.
Then little by little
George became ready
to work again.

The first month
he didn't push himself.
The second month
he moved a little faster.
By the third month,
George was working
as much as ever.

One morning
on his way
to the third restaurant
he felt a little sick.
He parked his car
and made his way inside.
No sooner
did he open the door

than everything went black.
He couldn't stay on his feet.
Without a word,
he fell to the floor
like a rag doll.

Cleo was there
at the time.
She ran over
to see what was wrong.
"Bamba! Bamba!"
she cried,
patting him on the face.
"Call a doctor!"
she called to a busboy.
"He's out like a light!"

It was ten minutes
before the ambulance
got to the restaurant.
By then, it was too late.
"I know he's gone,"
Cleo told the ambulance staff.

"We'll take him anyway,"
they said.

"All right,"
said Cleo.
"Let me just empty his pockets."

Andy walked in
just as Cleo said that.
"Here's his money,"
she said to her husband.
"Here are his cards.
And what's this—
a little gray stone?"

"Oh, my God,"
said Andy.
"I've seen that stone before!
Bamba showed it to me
when I was a child.
It's from Greece.
He brought it with him
the first time
he came to America!"

"He's carried it with him
all these years,"
said Cleo.
"That's really something."

Andy took the stone
in his hand.
"Sometimes Bamba
could be a hard-head,"
he cried.
"But only a man
with a soft heart
would carry a stone
from his first home
all these years."

"I think that stone
stands for Bamba's Greek heart,"
said Cleo.
"It was always
a part of him."

"Bamba's Greek heart
will always be a part
of us and these restaurants,"
Andy said.
And with that,
George's son
put the little round stone
in his own pocket.

Thinking It Over

1. In your family,
   what do you do
   when an older family member
   needs special care?

2. Do you have a special something
   that you have kept
   for a long time?

3. Think of the different meanings
   of the word *heart*.
   What ideas
   can you come up with?

4. Do you know anyone
   who has always kept
   a part of his or her heart
   in another place?